DESIG

Product Design

Stephanie Atkinson
& Clive Mockford

Oxford University Press

INTRODUCTION

Product Design has been prepared and written with the design and technology student as the prime audience, although we hope that all students in secondary education may find it useful.

We have sought to describe and clarify the processes inherent in the design and development of products in whatever area of technology they are based. All designers operate within a framework. Making this framework evident and meaningful to students who are learning about design is a vital part of their education. Showing also that no one system or design methodology can lead to a successful outcome is, we believe, an equally important aspect of the education of young designers.

Stephanie Atkinson, Clive Mockford 1991

Oxford University Press, Walton Street, Oxford OX2 6DP

Oxford   New York   Toronto
Delhi   Bombay   Calcutta   Madras   Karachi
Petaling Jaya   Singapore   Hong Kong   Tokyo
Nairobi   Dar es Salaam   Cape Town
Melbourne   Auckland

and associated companies in
Berlin   Ibadan

Oxford is a trade mark of Oxford University Press

First published 1991

A CIP catalogue record for this book is available from the British Library.

ISBN 0 19 832784 6

Typeset in News Gothic by
Tradespools Ltd, Frome, Somerset
Printed in Singapore

Acknowledgements

J Allan Cash pp 6 (top left), 8 (left); **Dixons plc** pp 52 (top right), 53 (top right); **S&R Greenhill** p 10 (bottom left); **Science Photo Library** pp 4, 26, 47 (right); **Tropix Photo Library** p 36 (left).

Additional photography by **Peter Gould** and **Chris Honeywell**.

Special thanks to Nick Rose and St Augustines School, Iffley, Oxford.

Illustrations by **Tony Ansell, Colin Elgie, Linda Jeffrey, Peter Richardson** and **Julie Tolliday**.

CONTENTS

What is a product?

A product is anything designed and made to serve a purpose. We buy products to use in our homes, at work, and in our leisure time.

When designing, there are two main types of product:

■ **Type 1** innovations – totally new products.

■ **Type 2** remodellings of existing products.

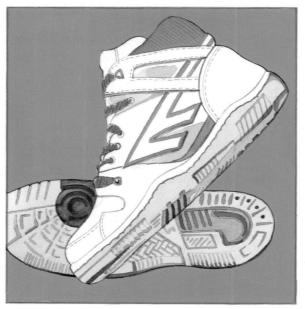

Most of the product design in industry is of the second type.

New products or new models are often the result of one or more of the following:

■ invention of new technical components;

■ development of new materials;

■ new **styling** to attract previous customers.

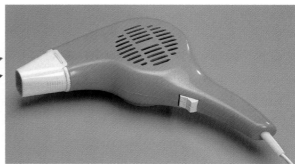

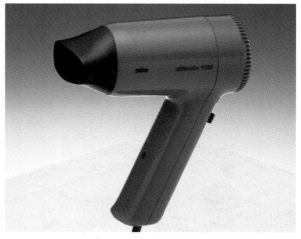

Products that we buy in the shops range from washing machines, hairdryers, and music centres to trainers, toothbrushes, and garden tools. All products go through the same type of process before they reach the consumer.

Designers and manufacturers spend a lot of time and money in researching, designing, making, advertising, and marketing their products. They hope, by doing this, to make their product answer the needs of as many people as possible, so that their sales will be high.

The designer and human needs

Basic human needs are for food, shelter, clothing, and safety. People also have needs of a different type, such as the need for self expression and the need to belong. Products are designed and made to answer these needs.

Shelter

Food

Clothes

Self expression

Safety

Belonging

Products must be fit for the purpose for which they are intended – they must provide shelter, self expression, or whatever need they are designed for. If you are designing for one individual, it can be easy to take all the relevant design considerations into account. But professional designers and manufacturers usually try to satisfy many different customers with the same product. Sometimes they find this difficult to achieve.

Some products must be fashionable to bring their owners the respect of others. If they are designed to last too long, it may mean they are thrown away before they are worn out.

ASSIGNMENTS

● Think of products that you have bought recently. Name one that is a totally new product – an innovation – and one that is a remodelling of an existing product.

● Think of a product that you have replaced with a new model recently. List the differences between the new and the old product. Why do you think each of the changes was made?

● Name the products that you own that you are proud of. Which need(s) do they answer?

● Draw a product that you own which you feel shows your need for self expression.

5

The designer in action

A designer works to create ideas and to turn these ideas into a product. The original suggestion for a product is given to the designer by a **client**. The client may be a company, an individual, or in school it may be your teacher.

In industry, the product will need to be well designed if the company is to be successful. The designer has a great deal of responsibility, and can make the difference between success and failure for the company.

Designers may work on their own or as part of a team of people. Each person on the team may be given a small part of a problem to work on.

When the designer starts work on a new project, he or she meets the client to obtain a description of exactly what is needed. This description is written down and is called a **brief**. The brief describes the problem but does not tell the designer how to solve it, or even whether it can be done.

Designers, like detectives, need to find out as much about the brief as possible. Two ways that they can do this are by:

- talking to the client;
- looking at similar products.

Already the designer may be starting to think of ways to overcome the problem.

At this stage the designer normally writes a product design **specification**. This states all the things which the product needs to do. It may also include any tests which should be performed on the product, and details of any regulations which must be considered.

Now comes the creative part. The designer continues to gather information, thinking of ideas, drawing, writing notes down, even making models to try to find answers. Sometimes the way forward appears in a flash. At other times a lot of hard work and thought is needed before a solution to a problem is found.

Even when you have found a way forward with a problem, there is still much more work to be done. More models may need to be made. People who will use the product may need to test the models to see if the idea works. The designer may talk to the client about his or her ideas while doing this development work. **Evaluating** a design at this stage can be difficult and can take a long time.

Finally, the whole project is presented to the client for assessment. The client then decides which of the following to do:

■ go ahead and make the product;

■ ask for more work to be carried out by the designer;

■ stop the project completely.

Being a designer means you need to consider many different things at the same time, and to suggest a variety of ways to reach a solution. The chapters that follow tell you more about the pieces of the designer's jigsaw puzzle, and help you fit them together.

ASSIGNMENTS

● Imagine that you have been given a brief to design a new seat for use by people sitting at a computer terminal. List all the stages your work would involve and suggest how much time you might spend on each.

● Think of three different products used for boiling water in the kitchen. Put yourself in the position of the designer of these products, and decide which one to use for the following groups of people:

a) mothers of young children.   **b)** elderly people.

List all the things you considered when making your choice. Can you suggest any improvements which can be made to these products?

Getting started

A designer gets information about a project first of all by reading a design brief and discussing this with the client. The brief describes a problem. Sometimes it provides very little other information.

An example of a design brief is shown below.

Design Brief

An eye shield is required for premature babies that have to undergo ultraviolet light treatment as a cure for jaundice.

After thinking about the project, the designer needs to decide whether it can be tackled with the resources available, such as the time for the project, the number of people who can work on it, and the budget that is available. Some preliminary research may help in deciding this.

If the designer accepts the project, he or she should then write a product design specification. Further research is needed, to make sure the designer has a clear statement of exactly what the product has to do. A successful product will usually have had all its requirements clearly identified before detail design work starts.

Guidelines for producing this specification are available from many books on the design process. These guidelines cover areas like the ones illustrated below.

As you investigate the project, you will find all sorts of different pieces of information which may help when you consider solutions to the problem. Being immersed in a problem can be extremely useful for the designer. It can help you decide what a product needs to do and how it should be assessed.

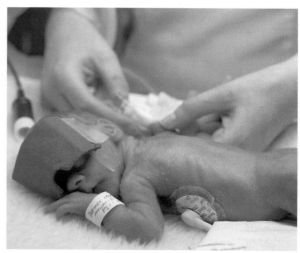

A baby with jaundice receiving treatment

It may seem very time consuming to collect all this information together and write it down, when all you want to do is start designing. Remember, though, if the rules for organizing the project are not clear then the designer and client may not agree on the type of product which is being developed. A soft toy might turn into a robot overnight!

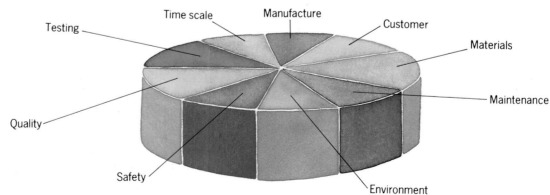

Time scale · Manufacture · Testing · Customer · Materials · Quality · Maintenance · Safety · Environment

Areas a product design specification should cover

The client will require the designer to complete the work by a certain deadline. To make sure that this is what happens, the designer has to find out exactly how much time is available for the project, and to plan what is going to be done and when. This information can be presented in the form of a planning chart, and this helps to make sure that everything works according to schedule.

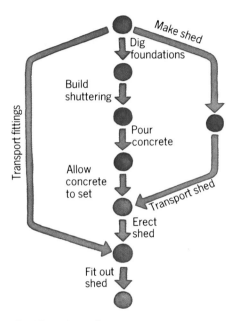

A simple planning chart

For example, you might have a client who needs a light fitting designed for a new type of light bulb. The new bulb will be available in one month's time. You will have all the details of the new bulb, along with other research, such as the market for which it is intended, the target price, etc. If your client is going to start selling this new product before the competitors you will need to work quickly. Supplying your client with the finished design work on time is vital.

ASSIGNMENTS

● Choose a design project which you have recently completed. Write down all the stages which you went through and against each stage indicate how much time you spent on that part of the work.
Present your answer in the form of a chart.

● A designer needs to keep in close touch with the client, to make sure that the design which is being developed matches up to the needs of the client. The designer needs to demonstrate ideas to the client and explain clearly what is being developed. List as many ways as you can which the designer can use to do this.

● Think of a design problem and write out a design brief which describes it. Pass this to one of your friends, and ask him or her to describe to you what the design problem is. Does your friend understand the problem? If not, find out which parts of your brief are not clear, and try to improve them.

Getting ideas

From the moment a designer is presented with a problem, many possible solutions will come to mind. Human beings can find it difficult to stop thinking of ways round things! The designer will try to think of as many ideas as possible and to log these.

There are several things which can be done to help obtain different ideas. You might try the following:

■ go to a library and find as many books on the subject as possible;

■ talk to people about the problem and see what ideas they have;

■ watch people using an existing product or system;

■ look at other similar products or systems.

Having all these ideas and pieces of information around can seem confusing, but designers will be able to use this situation to come up with new ideas. You may find an idea springs to mind at the most unlikely moment!

One thing is certain: information helps designers to consider and manipulate ideas in the search for an answer. Be careful, and consider as many ways of looking at the task as possible. Answers come from all sorts of different directions. The more routes you try, the more the chance of success.

The designer will need to choose solutions that match the requirements of the customer. To decide this, the designer may need to check the product design specification, or to complete further research.

Once you have selected which of your design ideas is the best solution to the problem, you may feel that you are finished. This is not the case. Many details need to be considered. A number of difficult decisions may still need to be made. For example:

■ which materials will be best for each part or component?

■ what size will each component be?

■ once the sizes of individual components are worked out, is the overall size of the product still acceptable?

■ which manufacturing process will be best to produce each component?

■ are there any fittings, such as hinges, to be used? If so, they need to be chosen from the wide selection available.

■ what finish is going to be suitable for each part of the product?

The designer needs to find and evaluate various solutions to each of these questions before a model is produced to show the client.

The next stage is to produce the model to show the client. This can be in any one of three forms:

■ a block model, which looks just like the product but is solid and has no working parts. This sort of model will allow the client to see and feel what the product will be like overall. It may not allow the client to use it;

■ a working model, which looks like, feels like, and works like the product, but is made from materials and processes that are cheaper than the final mass-produced product;

■ a **prototype**, which is made from the correct materials and processes.

These models may be made the exact size of the product. In some cases the product will be very small or large and a scale model will be needed.

A scale model being photographed for the designer

It is vital that the model is well made. Otherwise, the designer and the client will not be able to evaluate correctly how well the product answers the brief, and how well it suits the market for which it is intended.

Deciding details and making models

11

Evaluation

Throughout the design process, the designer will be involved in evaluation. While researching the problem, he or she needs to evaluate the information collected together. During designing, it is important for the designer to evaluate and modify his or her thoughts continually.

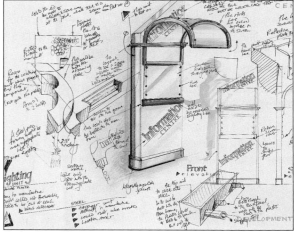

A design sheet

During the making of a model or a prototype, small or sometimes large changes may be essential. This could be because of the process and the materials available, or because it can be difficult to imagine what the product will really look like until it is made in three dimensions.

When the prototype is finished, the designer, the client, and a user of the product need to evaluate the solution. This is most important. The company needs to be sure that the product will serve the purpose for which it was intended. They will not want to spend large amounts of money on making the product if it does not work. A very pleasing chair to look at is no use if it is too small and is uncomfortable.

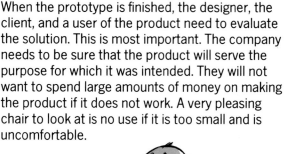

While designing a product, the designer will evaluate mostly in the form of written notes or drawings. Once the product is made, videos of it in use or tape recordings of interviews with users are often helpful for the designer. Sound judgements on any improvements that are needed can then be made.

Presenting your work

Product designers must be able to communicate their ideas to a variety of people involved in the project.

To make sure that their idea is put into production, designers will spend many hours on presenting their final solutions. Any of the following may be appropriate:

■ very high quality presentation drawings;

■ scale models or full size prototypes;

■ photographs of scale models which can look like the 'real thing'.

■ a report to explain details of the proposed design.

In your design work in school it is very important that you present your ideas professionally. You must be able to communicate your ideas and solutions in a form that will impress whoever looks at them. You have to 'sell' your ideas to your teacher or client.

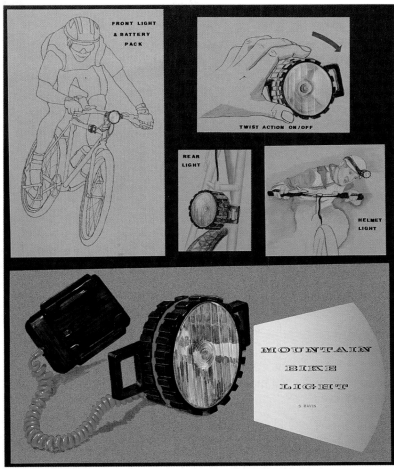

A presentation drawing for a mountain bike light

● Imagine you are designing a child's pushchair. List as many products as you can which you might look at for ideas. Refer to the drawing of trolleys on page 10.

● Make a list of materials that would be suitable to make an egg cup from. Give reasons for your choices.

● From your kettle at home, work out a list of features that you think are important to have in a good kettle design. Using this list, work out a questionnaire that you could use to ask friends and relatives how well designed their kettle is.

● Visit your local shopping centre and find a product that you feel is being promoted well. Sketch the display stand that is being used, and write a description explaining why you feel it is successful.

Talking to clients

A designer in industry will have a client to design for. When you are looking for a project at school, you will find there are many advantages if you too have a 'real' client. This might be an old person who needs a product to help them live a normal life, or a local playschool with a storage problem.

At the start of the project, you will be able to ask your clients what they feel are the important points that need to be considered. This will help you to build up a clear picture of what your design must achieve.

When you visit your clients, you will need to record your questions and answers and any helpful sketches, so that you may refer to them while you are designing. You must work out a list of questions to ask your clients before you go, so as not to take up too much of their time. You will find that your clients' answers will lead to other questions which you will also find helpful to ask.

It will help you if you visit your client several times throughout your design project. This might be:

■ for further guidance and advice once you have analysed the information you have received;

■ to allow the client to evaluate the project at different stages, by looking at your drawings and trying out any mock-up models that you have made;

■ to help you to check for mistakes in your decision making before you get too far and it becomes too late to change your idea.

Looking at similar products

An important part of research is looking at existing products that have been manufactured to answer similar needs. You should do this because:

■ there is not a single answer to the design of a product;

■ different designers see their way to a solution from different angles and therefore end up with different solutions;

■ different designers see different aspects of the brief as being important;

■ different materials and techniques of manufacture alter an answer to a product problem.

'Looking at' means evaluating these other solutions to your brief. It will give you a checklist of:

■ features you do not feel are important to include in your solution;

■ features you feel may be useful to include in your solution;

■ features that you know you need to improve to make your answer even more successful than the product you are looking at.

To carry out this research, you should look at examples in shops, and check *Which?* reports to see if they have done any tests on your type of product. Try similar products out at friends' and relatives' homes, if you can. Then use a questionnaire to ask other people their opinions about existing products that they own.

This should help you to make sound judgements. You are not looking at the existing products to find an answer so that you can copy it!

Different designs for a product answering the same need

ASSIGNMENTS

● Interview local designers. Ask them about their work and how they communicate with their clients.

● Imagine that you are about to design a burglar alarm. Go into your local town and find as many examples of burglar alarms as you can. Make sketches and notes to refer to. Then work out a list of questions that you would ask a designer who has produced one of the burglar alarms you have seen.

● Using a product that you have at home, such as an iron or a kettle, make a list of all the good points of its design and another list of all the bad points.

● **a)** Look at as many different hairdryers as you can, and make a list of all the features a good hairdryer should have.

b) Taking a hairdryer that you have at home, find out how well your hairdryer compares to the list you have made.

Looking at earlier models

One good way of learning about how products have developed is to take a particular product and look at the way it has changed through history. This will help the designer to find out why certain features have been used in current designs. It might also point out some unsuccessful things, which were tried but did not work.

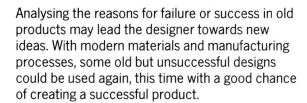

Looking at earlier products can help the designer

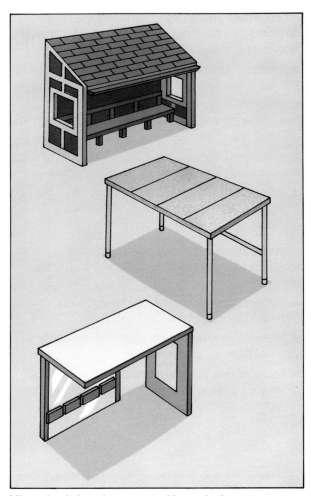

Historical development of bus shelters

Analysing the reasons for failure or success in old products may lead the designer towards new ideas. With modern materials and manufacturing processes, some old but unsuccessful designs could be used again, this time with a good chance of creating a successful product.

An example of this type of activity might be to investigate designs for a bus shelter. Looking at structures and small seating or standing areas might reveal all sorts of different features. These will make the designer more aware of what has gone before and how improvements could be made.

The places where you can complete this type of work are normally libraries and museums. Some museums specialize in certain areas of design and have particular collections of products. Many reference books are available about different types of product. These may also be of use in finding out about products which have been used in the past.

Other places to find earlier models and answers to briefs you are set are in your own homes, those of grandparents, or those of neighbours. What you need to do is go out and look!

A product design specification is written in order to have a clear agreement between the designer and the client about the product which is to be designed. To help the designer to write this specification, guidelines are available from organizations such as SEED (Sharing Experiences in Engineering Design). These set out different areas which need to be considered – see page 18 for some of these.

Product Design Specification

1. User
The item should be suitable for all bicyle users (do not include the tricycle)

2. Consultation
Bicycle shops or agents should be consulted and asked for information or catalogues.

3. Safety
• The item must meet all the safety standards (BS Standard), particularly with respect to toxicity, force resistance, sharp corners and edge protection.
• The manufacturing method must pass the BS Standard testing.
• Sharp corners and edges should be avoided.
• The design of any hinges, folding bars and arms, mechanisms must not allow fingers or part of the human body to be trapped.
• The bicycle should not be easy to push or pull down by an adult normally or accidentally when the bicycle is held by the item.

4. Ergonomics
• The main aim of the storage system is to make bicyles easy to be stored by the age above 6 years old.
• The design for the join system should allow using by people above 6 years old.
• The weight of the item should stand stably and also should be easy to be moved out singly.

5. Materials
• Any material used should be non-toxic.
• Materials selected must be durable.
• Materials should be easy to clean.

Part of a product design specification

The product design specification describes the limitations which the designer must work to, such as cost. It also describes how the product should work. This information can be used during the design work, and on completion of the project. It will allow the designer to test what has been made to see if it meets the client's requirements.

Designers normally create product design specifications by looking at a standard checklist of all of the factors which need to be considered. Once all the research about what is required has been done, this checklist can be filled in. Not all of the sections in the list will be appropriate for your design problem. You will need to choose which factors are required for your specific task.

The quality of your research will affect how useful the product design specification is. If you miss out one vital piece of information, it could mean that your product may not work as the client intended. The washing machine which was supposed to spin clothes at 1000 revolutions per minute may only spin them at 100 revolutions per minute if the speed was not in the product design specification. That is very slow!

The specification may need to be written several times. The client and designer may not agree at first about what is to be produced or how it should be evaluated.

Remember, the product design specification should act as a reference against which you test all your product ideas to see if they match up to the client's requirements. It is a very important document.

Factors in the product design specification

These factors will probably include:

- performance – how fast, how slow, how often, what loads it will withstand (dynamic or static), etc;

- interaction with environment
    – temperature range, vibration level, how dirty, etc;

- life in service – how long the service life of the product should be;

- maintenance – when maintenance will be required, how access to parts is provided, etc.

Other factors to consider may include: √ x

	√ x
target product cost	☐
competition	☐
delivery	☐
packing	☐
quantity	☐
manufacturing facility	☐
size	☐
weight	☐
aesthetics, appearance, finish	☐
materials	☐
product life span	☐
British Standards	☐
ergonomics	☐
customer information	☐
quality and reliability	☐
shelf life	☐
time scales	☐
testing	☐
safety	☐
company constraints	☐
market constraints	☐
patents, literature, and product data	☐
political and social implications	☐

Budgeting

One major aspect of design work is making sure that a **budget** is given to a project and that the designer keeps to this budget. The budget will state the amount of money that can be spent on the whole project. It may also give an estimate for the cost of different stages of the project, such as research, modelling, etc.

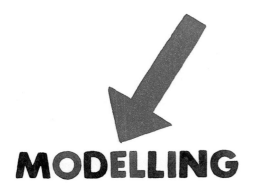

RESEARCH

TESTING

?

BUDGET

DESIGNING

MODELLING

Some of the factors which make up the total design budget

The overall budget for the project will be decided by the client when the designer is given the project to work on. The client may ask the designer to give an estimate of the cost of the design work before giving permission for work to begin. Other designers or groups of designers may also be asked to give an estimate of how much money they would charge to complete the work.

In these circumstances the client will then agree a price for the work with the designer who is to carry out the work. This would limit the amount of time the designer can spend on the work, the cost of modelling materials, the cost of paying other technical specialists for advice, etc.

Once the budget has been agreed, the designer needs to be careful to manage the money in order to produce the work for the client at the agreed price.

Planning

Planning the project allows the designer to work out what the overall cost of the project might be. It is useful to refer to a detailed plan when discussing this with the client. This will help the designer to manage the project and achieve the financial and time targets which the client has set.

Project planning normally starts with the designer making a list of all the stages which need to be completed during the project. Some activities, such as research, will be given a period of time in which they need to be completed. Once the time for an activity is known then a cost can be worked out. This costing is made up mainly of the following:

■ the payment to the person who is to carry out the task;

A civil engineer at work

■ the overheads connected with that person – things such as the cost of heating the building in which he or she works, the materials used for writing letters, etc;

A design studio

■ the materials that person will require to complete the task – perhaps the cost of expensive computers, modelling materials, etc.

Modelling materials

All this detailed planning needs to be carried out if the project is to keep to the budget which has been agreed with the client.

Computers can be used to help the designer with these aspects of project planning. A computer program could help with:

■ placing events in the correct order of activity;

■ giving time to each activity;

■ giving resources in the form of people to each activity;

■ giving costs for the resources.

The computer can then calculate the overall cost of the project, when events are scheduled. This plan can be changed and adapted by the designer until a suitable schedule with the correct cost is achieved.

ASSIGNMENTS

● Draw up a list of the factors which you think will be important as part of the product design specification for the following products:

a) bicycle **b)** a kitchen storage unit **c)** a climbing frame for children aged 5 to 12

For each product, place the factors in rank order according to how important you think they will be. What differences, if any, can you see between the areas that will matter most in the specifications for the three products?

● The following activities are part of the first part of the product design process:

drawing up a specification; collecting the brief from client;
costing the whole project; conducting initial research;
discussing the problem with the client; planing the time available.

Place these activities in the order in which you would need to carry them out. (Some activities might take place at the same time as others.)

Present your answer in the form of a bar chart, with 'Activities' on the vertical axis, 'Time' on the horizontal axis, and a horizontal bar for each activity. The position of each bar will represent when it starts and finishes.

Research

As a designer you will need to investigate many things while you are designing, such as different materials and **human factors**. Research goes on throughout designing. Finding out about the brief and the specification during the early stages of designing involves research. After that, the designer needs to look at things which might help to solve the problem which is being tackled.

This might involve further research into detailed aspects of similar products or previous models, building on information which you collected as part of your work with the product design specification. To gather research information, a designer might do any of the following:

■ carry out small experiments on components or parts which may be used in a design;
■ collect information from libraries about things which will affect the design;
■ write to companies to collect information. Perhaps a visit to some of these companies may be required to find out more;
■ talk to users of a particular product to find out what they really need.

Finding information and being able to use it can be very helpful when working out your design. Ideas will be forming in your mind as to how you might solve the whole problem. As the designer, you will need to find out many things about these ideas and whether they will work.

Materials, mechanisms, finishes such as paint, varnish, etc., all need to be investigated so that you can find out about all the aspects which go together to form your design.

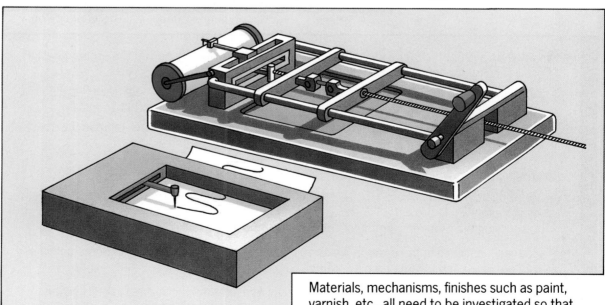

Tensile testing a sample of material to be used for a product

The users of a product may need to be asked a number of questions to see if they require particular features in a design. They may be able to tell the designer about things which are wrong with their current model. A questionnaire or a series of interviews with users might provide this information.

How the product is going to be made is often a very important factor. The designer will need to find out about production processes, which might be altogether new or which he or she might not have used before.

An injection moulding machine

Research can involve a lot of reading

The designer will gather a large amount of information in order to understand the constraints of the problem and the resources which are available.

Collecting the information is not enough. It needs to be sorted and stored in some form of organized filing system. You might make an index to the information which has been collected, using a number of different headings. This could be on a computer database.

Most important of all, the designer needs to read and understand the pieces of information. They may give him or her a better picture of what is required. This will be an advantage in designing the new product, since it can be designed with the problems corrected or with new features added.

Developing ideas

A designer often finds it difficult to switch off from thinking about a design problem. Ideas occur at all stages of the design process. A good designer will always log information and make sure that ideas are not lost.

As a designer, you will need to make sure that you do not forget ideas. Carrying a notebook is often helpful, both for sketching and developing design ideas and for making notes about any thoughts you have.

Hopefully, ways in which you can solve the whole problem or just small parts of the problem will have been occurring to you from the moment when you were set the brief. You will need to start working on these by sketching on paper and possibly modelling.

Try to put as many ideas down on paper or in your notebook as possible. Good designs sometimes emerge from the most curious ideas. Once a designer has started sketching ideas on paper, all sorts of other ideas or modifications come to mind. These can be sketched out onto the design sheet and can lead to further modifications.

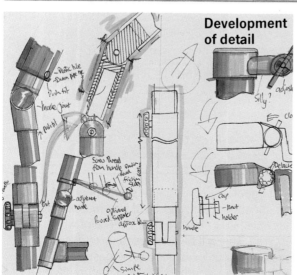

Development of detail

If a designer gets a mental block about how to tackle a problem, there are a number of things which can be done to help:

■ draw out a **mind map** (or brainstorm), writing down all your thoughts on the problem or parts of the problem as they occur to you;

■ leave the problem for a short while. Work on something else or have a break. When you come back to the problem you will see it in a different way and may be able to make progress;

■ talk to people about your ideas so far, or about the problems which you are experiencing. You could talk to your parents, a friend, your teacher, or a professional designer or engineer. Talking about what you are doing will perhaps give you more ideas or show you a new way forward.

All designers have individual ways of working. You will need to try out different methods for yourself in order to find out which method suits you best.

When developing ideas you may find it essential to go and find out about things which you did not look at as part of your initial research. This might be information about how to make something, which materials to use, etc.

Mitred haunched mortice and tenon joint

Square haunched mortice and tenon joint

Dowel joint

Bridle joint

Methods of joining wooden rails to legs

If your product is to be used by a certain group of people, there may be some further questions you wish to ask them once you have completed some design work. A model of a product might be produced to test your idea on people and obtain their reactions.

Testing of a product

During this period of development the designer creates, tests, and modifies ideas. Changes are made, improvements added, unsuccessful things removed, new ideas drawn up. All the time, the aim is to find out the best way to overcome the problems and produce a design which will match up to the specification for the product.

ASSIGNMENTS

● Work out all the things that you would need to find out about if you were to design an iron which could be used on holiday. Draw out a mind map to help in getting ideas, then draw up a list.

● Imagine you are designing a clothes peg which can be used by elderly people. Draw up some initial ideas for solving this problem. How could you test whether your ideas would work?

Group working

Designing on your own can be great fun and very enjoyable. The results can often be a successful innovation or an improvement on a particular product. But you may not have the specialist knowledge to design the whole of a product.

In industry, designers often work as part of teams or groups. The group can be made up of different specialists. There might be:

■ an electrical engineer to design and develop the internal workings of a product;

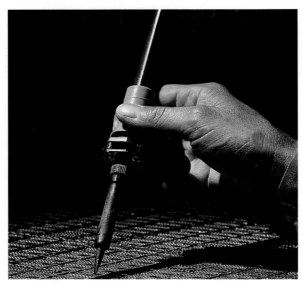

■ a production engineer to work out how the product will be made;

■ an industrial designer to design the outside form of the product and make it usable.

The number of people in the team and their individual expertise can vary. The benefit of working in a team with lots of experts is that you may design a more complex and possibly more successful product.

For a design group to work well and to produce a successful product, the people in it must work together as a team. Managing this situation calls for a special type of person, who may be a designer but who also has responsibility for leading the team of people. The manager or team leader will be responsible for giving tasks to each person in the group and making sure that they keep to their targets.

Creating a design team is like the manager of a sports team trying to select which people to put in the team to give the best group performance. One person may be a brilliant individual, but may not be able or willing to play as part of a team and share his or her skill for the benefit of the whole team. Selecting a team is a difficult process.

Working in teams is the normal method for professional designers in industry in the field of product design. It is very different from working on your own, and requires other skills than just being a good designer.

Selecting a team

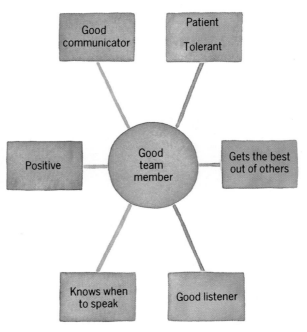

Members of the team may not all be based in the same company. People who have special skills may be required. They are often called **consultants** and are asked to complete a small part of the design work which the rest of the team cannot do.

ASSIGNMENTS

● Organize yourselves into groups of three or four people. Each group should try to work out a solution to one of the following problems:

a) design the top for a dispenser of wood glue which does not become clogged up around the top when being used.

b) design an eraser with a fine point which can be used accurately on drawings.

How easy was it to get on with other people in the group? Did everyone help to develop and suggest ideas for solving the problem? Do you think that the answer which you came up with was better than if you had worked on your own?

Choosing the best approach

For each design project, a designer will need to choose the best method for achieving a successful result. A team approach may be best, or it might be that working as an individual, using consultants for special help, would be more productive.

A great deal will depend on what the project is. Designing a new computer would require a large team of designers and engineers. A package for a new cleaning material might be designed by an individual.

Complex products need teams of specialists

Simpler products may be better designed by one person

Once the organization of the project has been sorted out, the designer or design team must decide what would be the best method for developing the product. For example, designing a new **corporate identity** or **logo** for a company would require work mainly in two dimensions on paper.

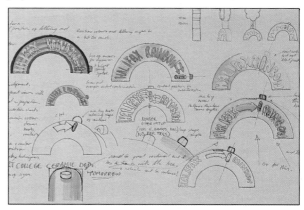

Working on a project to restyle the handle of a golf club or hairbrush, though, would involve the designer looking at three-dimensional forms. So it would be best to use models to design and evaluate solutions to this problem, or a computer to show three-dimensional, solid images, rather than spending a long time drawing on paper.

The designer must be careful to select an approach which suits the design brief which has been set. A person who can change his or her style of operation can often be a better designer than someone who goes through the same checklist of design stages for every project.

Evaluating design ideas

As ideas come to you and you note them down, you will be making decisions about how well they match up to the guidelines which were written down in the product design specification.

Some ideas will be discarded once you have thought about them. Others will need to be considered more carefully. Experts might need to be brought in to comment on the design. A model might need to be tested with the people who are going to use the product.

Testing a model of the product with the intended user

If you have several designs, it may be difficult to decide which one to develop further. You might choose to draw up a checklist of the most important factors from the product design specification, and give a rating for each design on a range of 1 to 10. A total score for each design can then be calculated. This would enable you to make an overall assessment, showing the design which matches up best to the product design specification.

Factors	Design 1	Design 2	Design 3
Ease of use	1	2	4
Colour	3	9	6
Price	7	7	4
Safety	4	3	7
Wear	4	1	5
Total	19	22	26

A design selection method

All the time you are designing, you make decisions and evaluate ideas. The professional designer needs to make sure that the decisions he or she takes are correct and based on the best evidence available.

ASSIGNMENTS

● **a)** Consider a lighting system for a bicycle. How might you decide whether a design is satisfactory and acceptable to the consumer? List as many factors as you can which could be used to assess the design.

b) Choose three different types of cycle lighting system and draw up a chart to show the overall rating of each, using the factors which you wrote down as an answer to the first part of this question. Give each system a score for every factor. You should end up with an overall score for each lighting system, showing which scores highest.

● The television and radio are answers to human needs. Describe what you think those needs are, and how each of the systems satisfies the needs.

Using sketches

Designers need to be able to communicate their ideas. They need to be able to talk about their ideas, write about them, and draw them.

Talking is not a permanent record, unless it is tape recorded. Writing a description of a design can take a long time, and may still be unclear.

Drawing is often an efficient method of communicating.

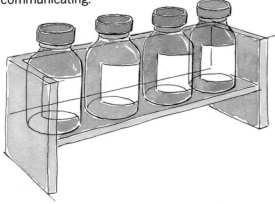

Designers need to record their thoughts so that they can:

■ show others what their ideas look like;

■ see for themselves what their ideas look like;

■ refer back to their ideas, in order to suggest further ideas and develop existing ones.

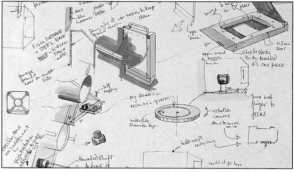

An early design sheet

In the early stages of designing, you need a quick method of drawing, as your ideas are changing fast. Later, as your ideas develop, your drawings will need to become careful and accurate.

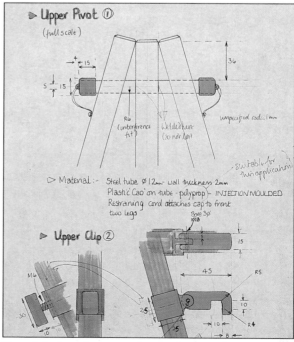

Careful sketches on a later design sheet

Sketching is a quick method of drawing freehand, without the use of equipment to help you. It is not difficult, but may require practice as it needs to look right. It is most important that the drawings represent your idea. To do this the drawings must be in proportion, although they do not need to be full size or to **scale**.

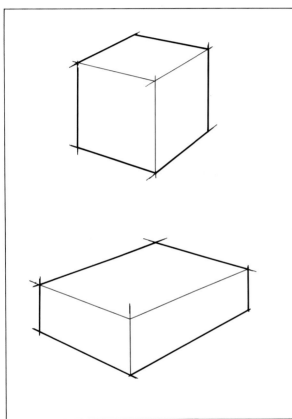

Which is the matchbox? Which is the sugar cube?

Your sketching might be:

■ a perspective sketch to show the whole product;

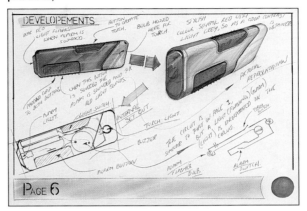

■ part of your design to explain a detail.

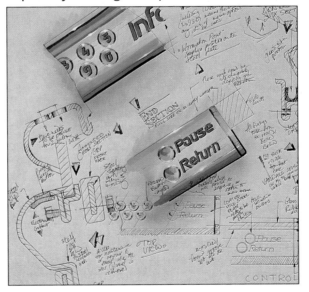

● Sketch a drinks can in perspective. Show all the lettering, remembering that it too needs to be in perspective.

● Take three rectangular items of different sizes, such as a block of butter, a packet of jelly, and a packet of sugar. Place them in a group and do a freehand perspective sketch, paying particular attention to the proportion of each item and its relationship to the others.

Drawing to scale

Sometimes sketching is not a precise enough method of drawing your ideas. While you are trying to think about design details you may need to:

■ work out exactly the dimensions of your material or methods of construction;

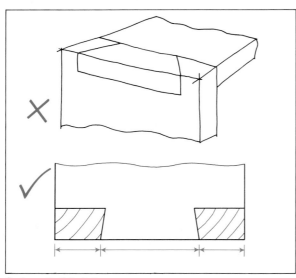

A dovetail joint

■ work out the exact measurement of part of your design to make sure it will fit into a set space;

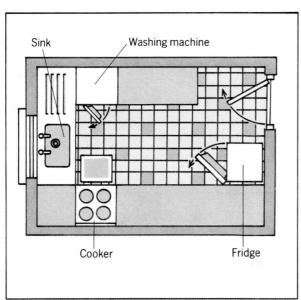

A kitchen layout

■ make certain that there is enough space between two parts of your design for fitting something in between.

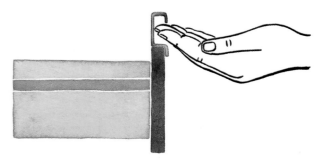

Side elevation of a kitchen drawer

In all these cases, producing an accurate working drawing may be the answer.

Sometimes, producing a full size working drawing would be a difficult task, as you might need a very large piece of paper. An architect, a boat builder, and a car designer all scale their drawings down. Printed circuit designers have to do the opposite and scale their drawings up.

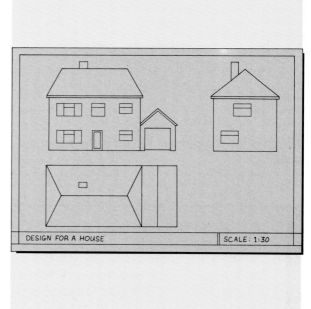

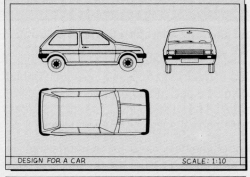

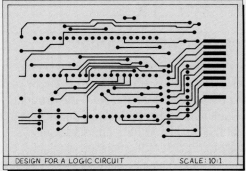

Selecting a scale

The scale to work to depends on the size of the object being drawn, and the size of the piece of paper to be drawn on. Choosing the scale means carefully working out what exactly is going to be drawn on the paper. The designer has to calculate how big that would be if drawn full size, then scale it down till it will fit on a suitable piece of paper comfortably, allowing space for measurements.

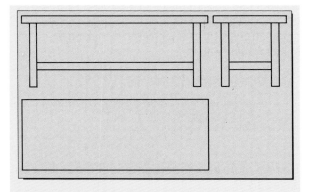

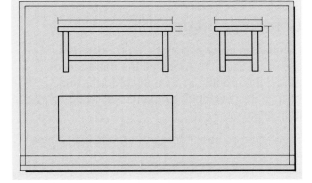

● Draw side **elevations** of the following products at a suitable scale so that each product will fit nicely on an A4 sheet of paper:

    a) a telephone.

    b) a car.

    c) your house.

● Draw a third angle **orthographic projection** of a matchbox at twice full size (2:1).

Using models

Models can be a useful method of representing your ideas. They can help you work out aspects of your design that are not easy to judge from a drawing. They can be used at various stages of the design process. There are several types available for the designer to use.

Mathematical models

These can help sort out such problems as the efficient use of materials. For example, they can tell the designer whether a product has been made strong/stiff enough without making it heavier than need be.

Mass = Density × Volume

e.g. Density of glass = 2600kg/cm^3 (2.6g/cm^3)
Volume of paperweight = 27cm^3
Mass of paperweight = $2.6 \text{g/cm}^3 \times 27 \text{cm}^3$
= 70.2 g

There is more about **mathematical modelling** on pages 38–9.

Computer models

Computers allow designers to produce both 2D and 3D models. They enable the designer to model the product in a variety of forms and change parts without having to redraw the whole item again.

There is more about computer models on pages 40–1.

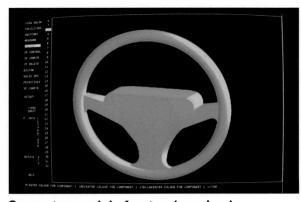

Computer model of a steering wheel

Two-dimensional models

These are very useful to explain how certain things work. The models are usually made of card of various colours so that different parts can easily be seen.

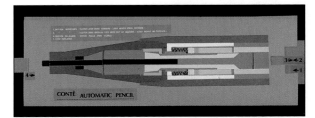

Model showing a section through a clutch pencil

Models of this type are usually a section through the item. The designer chooses a scale that is suitable to show the detail. Sometimes this may be twice normal size (2:1) or even bigger.

Very often the designer uses this modelling method to show a part of the product and not the whole thing.

Three-dimensional models

There are several types of three-dimensional model which allow the designer to see how parts of the product will work and what the product could look like. Some models are quick 'lash-ups' and not built to last. Others are made very carefully to represent the finished product.

The following pictures (below and opposite) show different types of three-dimensional model.

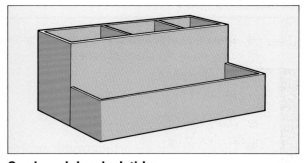

Card model: a desk tidy

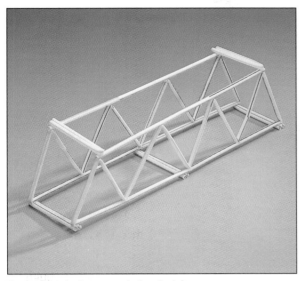

Straw and glue model: a bridge

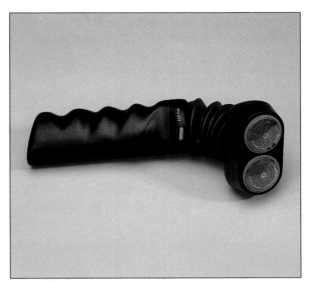

Block model: an electrical razor

Kit model: a gearing system

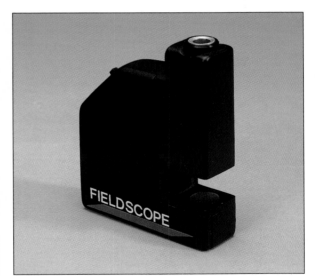

Working model: a field microscope

These modelling techniques will be described in more detail in chapter 6.

ASSIGNMENTS

● Using straws and pins, produce a model dining chair that is $^1/_4$ full size.

● Using card, make a scale model of a container that will hold three cassette tapes. The container should be able to be held in any way without the tapes falling out.

Using science

Science can be of great use to the designer. Gaining an understanding of the physical world can be very helpful when a decision needs to be made about such things as the correct material for a product.

For example, it may be that a strong, lightweight metal such as aluminium alloy has been chosen for a waterpump in a washing machine. By understanding materials science, the designer might be able to select a cheaper, stronger material. Perhaps a type of plastic would perform better than the material which had been chosen first.

A waterpump made out of metal and one made out of plastic

Science can show designers how products are affecting the world in which we live. Dangerous by-products or effects such as the depletion of the ozone layer can be reduced by the designer, once these problems and the damage which some products can cause are understood.

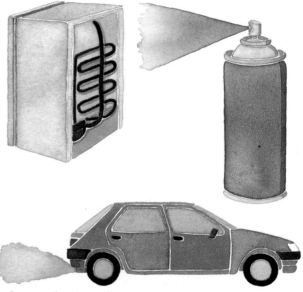

Atmospheric pollutants

Scientists who have made new materials have perhaps helped the designer most in developing better and new products. Materials such as carbon fibre or new adhesives have enabled new products to be successful.

Choosing a material for a product depends on three new factors:

■ the cost of the material;

■ the processes which can be used to turn the material into a new form or shape;

■ the physical properties of the material – whether it is ductile (that is, can be drawn into wires), has a high electrical resistance, or is toxic and cannot be used in a product designed for young children.

Science can help to inform the designer most about the third of these factors – the properties of a material.

Two very important factors which a designer must consider are the strength of a material, and a relationship between this and the density of the material.

The strength of a material can be found by using a scientific test, such as a **tensile test**. In this, the material is stretched until it breaks. The load (force) which is applied to the material is noted, along with the extension (stretch) of the sample at stages during the test.

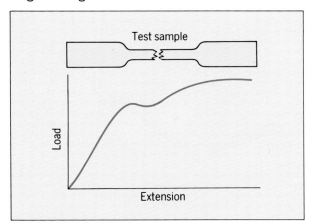

A tensile test sample and graph

Some materials behave in a very elastic way when stretched and can hold a high load before stretching permanently. Other materials can support only a very small load before they are permanently stretched, and do not return to their original size.

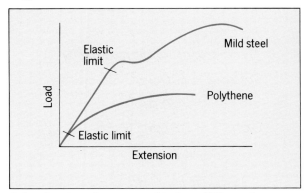

A load extension curve for two different materials

If the designer compares the information from tensile tests with the measurement of the density of a material, he or she can work out a value which will help when selecting materials for certain applications. This is the **strength to density value**. If a structure is required which is light but very strong, the designer should look for a material which has a high strength to density value.

Aluminium

Density = 2700 kg/m^3

Tensile strength = 40 N/mm^2

$$\text{Strength to density value} = \frac{\text{tensile strength}}{\text{density}}$$
$$= \frac{2700}{40}$$
$$= 67.5$$

Mild steel

Density = 7850 kg/m^3

Tensile strength = 240 N/mm^2

$$\text{Strength to density value} = \frac{\text{tensile strength}}{\text{density}}$$
$$= \frac{7850}{240}$$
$$= 32.7$$

Science will also allow the designer to consider how materials can be protected from the environment. If a garden rake is made of steel, then a finish will be required to protect parts of the rake from corrosion. Plating the rake with a non-ferrous coating such as chromium is one solution to this problem.

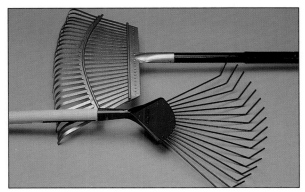

Garden rakes with different finishes

Using mathematics

Mathematics can be used by the designer to help when making decisions about parts of a design. The term which is often used when referring to the use of mathematics in design is mathematical modelling.

Mathematics can be seen as another resource which is available to the designer. Consider the design of the tread on a pair of step ladders. The designer has a number of decisions to make, such as which material should be used for maximum strength, cost, durability, etc., what shape the tread should be, and what thickness of material should be used. Decisions about materials may be helped by looking at scientific information. To compare different shapes for the tread and to work out what thickness of material to use, mathematics can be used.

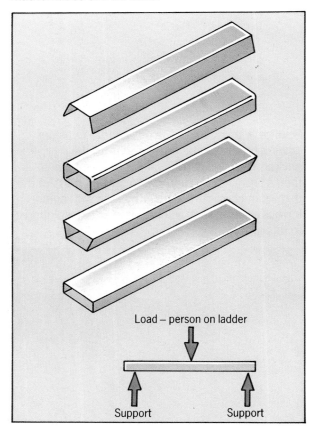

Different sections of metal for the tread of a step ladder

As a designer you may be involved with the design of casings for equipment. Part of the costing of the product will involve looking at the amount of material required to make each casing. Mathematics would be used to calculate this, and the results might lead towards the production of a cheaper product.

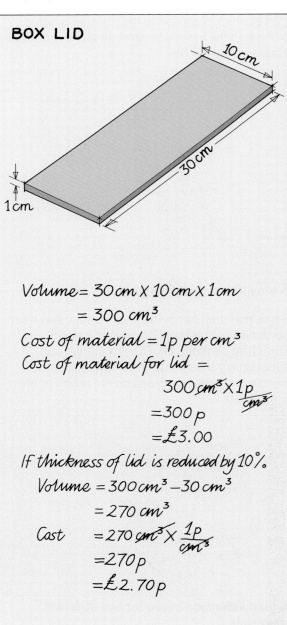

BOX LID

$$\text{Volume} = 30\,cm \times 10\,cm \times 1\,cm$$
$$= 300\ cm^3$$

Cost of material $= 1p$ per cm^3

Cost of material for lid $=$
$$300\,cm^3 \times 1p \over cm^3$$
$$= 300\,p$$
$$= £3.00$$

If thickness of lid is reduced by 10%
$$\text{Volume} = 300\,cm^3 - 30\,cm^3$$
$$= 270\ cm^3$$

Cost $= 270\,cm^3 \times \dfrac{1p}{cm^3}$
$$= 270\,p$$
$$= £2.70\,p$$

Textile designers use mathematics to work out the amount of material that is used in making a garment, and to estimate how many garments they need to sell before a profit is made. This information is vital if the product is to be successful and help the company to make a profit.

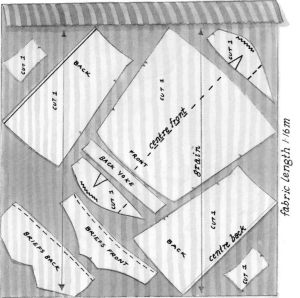

The pattern for a garment laid out on the fabric

In all areas of design, mathematics can help the designer to make better, more informed decisions about parts of a product. In industry, it may be necessary to call in a specialist at times to carry out this work. Even in your own design work the use of mathematics can improve the quality of your decision making.

ASSIGNMENTS

● **a)** Find out the density of the following materials:
concrete, steel, glass reinforced polyester, polythene, aluminium.
Calculate how much one cubic centimetre of each material would weigh.

b) Which of these five materials would be suitable to make a small boat out of? Using the list and your calculations, give your reasons why each material is or is not suitable for this purpose.

● A table top is 1.5 m long, 1 m wide and 10 mm thick. The designer of the table needs to inform the manufacturers how much varnish will be needed to coat each table top all over. The thickness of the varnish is 0.5 mm. How much varnish will be needed in litres to cover one table top?

Using computers

Computers can be used by the designer in a variety of ways:

- modelling the form of a product;
- modelling the mechanical or electrical behaviour of a product;
- helping to develop and update the drawings of a product;
- producing presentation drawings and advertising material;
- providing information for the designer about different aspects of the work, such as materials information, patents, etc;
- providing the designer with the means of producing professionally presented reports.

Computers can also be used as part of the **system** which manufactures a product. In a company that has a **computer integrated manufacturing system (CIM)**, design information can be passed through to the making stage – for example, information on the surface profile of a plastic bottle could be passed to the machine which makes the tools for the product. This puts the company in a good position to respond quickly to changes in the market, which can give the company a major advantage over its competitors.

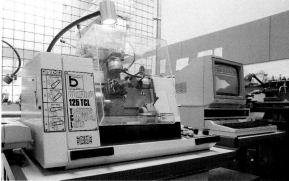

A computer controlled machining centre

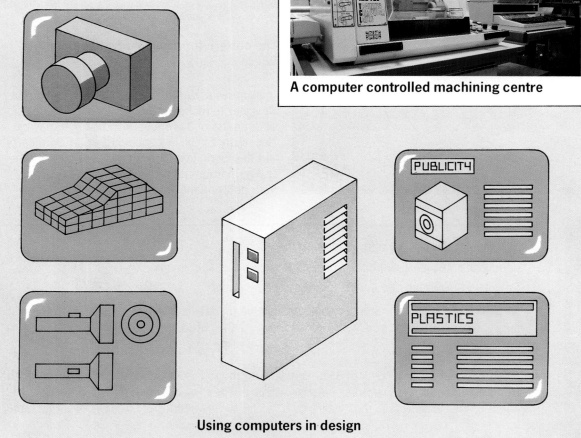

Using computers in design

The computer is used by the designer as a tool, just in the same way as you might use a camera to take pictures. The computer cannot design by itself. The designer manipulates ideas and information in order to look for a successful product. The computer can help to:

■ test out ideas about form;

■ carry out calculations concerned with performance;

■ create a **simulation** of a products operation.

A solid modelling system is just one example of a computer-based design tool. In this system, the designer inputs data about the form of a product, and the computer uses mathematics to generate a representation of the outside of the product. This is shown on the VDU screen. The designer can then instruct the computer to turn the image, so that it can be viewed from different angles, or to place it in different lighting conditions, give it a different surface finish, etc. Better, more informed decisions can then be made concerning the product. These should make it match the requirements of the specification closely, and help lead to a successful product.

This type of computer-based modelling has some clear advantages:

■ it can be set up by the designer quickly;

■ modifications can be made easily and the result observed;

■ different environments can be simulated for the product.

Information is vital if a designer is to create new, well-designed and functional products. It might be details of different types of adhesive or new electrical devices, or mathematical techniques for simulating the travel of a car through air. Accessing this information and searching for particular pieces of information can be made easier using computers.

Presenting design information to clients can also be a task where the computer can help designers. Manipulating two-dimensional images and text is a task which modern wordprocessors and pagemaking systems are good at. An image can be changed quickly and a professional copy produced ready for publication. Technology such as powerful desktop computers and laser printers has enabled the designer to be far more productive.

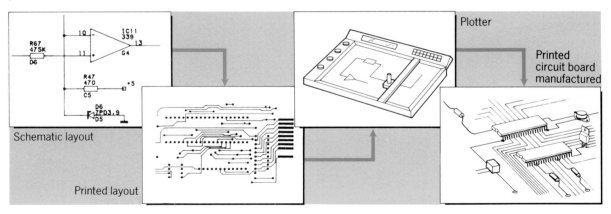

Schematic layout

Printed layout

Plotter

Printed circuit board manufactured

Working models

Making working models is a useful way of trying ideas out during the design process. Sometimes the designer is unable to be sure that the ideas on paper will actually work. Models that work can help. Sometimes the models are of parts of the design and sometimes they are of the whole product.

Models of part of the product may be produced during the design process to help the designer. They may also be produced by the designer to explain to the client how part of the product works.

Three different styles of knob for a radio

Full size working models of the whole product may be produced during the design process to see that everything fits into a product, and that it works and feels good to use. Sometimes these models are quick 'lash-ups'.

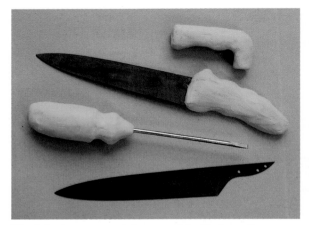

Models for screwdriver and knife handles

A full size working model may also be made at the end of the design process. This is called a working prototype. It is made to represent the finished product as nearly as possible, and will be used to test and evaluate how successful the chosen solution is. If it is successful it will be presented to the client as the designer's chosen solution.

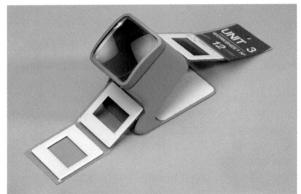

Working model of a slide viewer

Types of working model

Card is a suitable material for producing quick, simple mock-ups of ideas. It can be used to produce 2D working models of principles. It can also be used to give a 3D image. It can help you see the proportions of your product, although it may not be able to represent the feel or look of the real material.

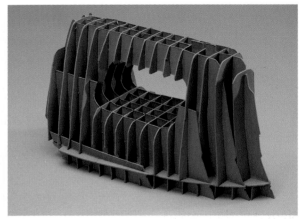

Model of an iron made out of card

Complex structures are far easier to work out in 3D than in a drawing. Straws are a quick, easy way of constructing them. Welding rod can give a stronger, more permanent structure, but it can take longer to produce the model.

Mechanical principles can quickly be modelled using kits, such as Meccano and Fishertechnic, and pneumatic circuits. Electronic circuits can be modelled and tested using kits like Locktronics, Alpha, and MFA.

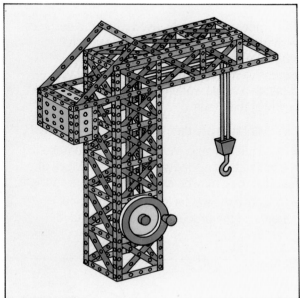

A Meccano model of a crane

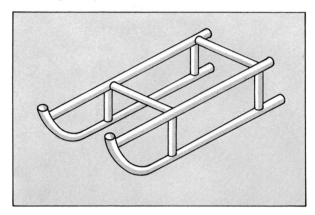

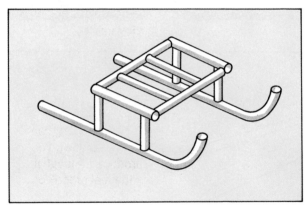

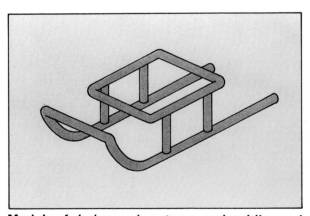

Models of sledges using straws and welding rod

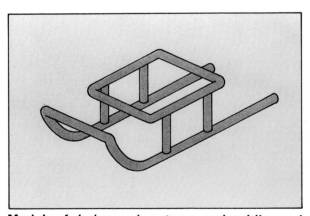

Modelling an electronic circuit

Block models

Materials such as polystyrene and MDF (medium density fibreboard) used in a block can allow the designer to model the 'solid form' of a product. This can be an important process, because it can help the designer to choose the correct form for the product.

The process can also be used when the designer wishes to show the client the chosen solution. Often the finished product will need very expensive manufacturing methods, and to produce a single working product would be too costly at this stage.

Disadvantages are that:

■ if handled, a solid model will rarely represent the feel of the finished product, as the block of material used may be either too heavy or too light;

■ because the model is a solid block, any 'innards' of the product will not be included.

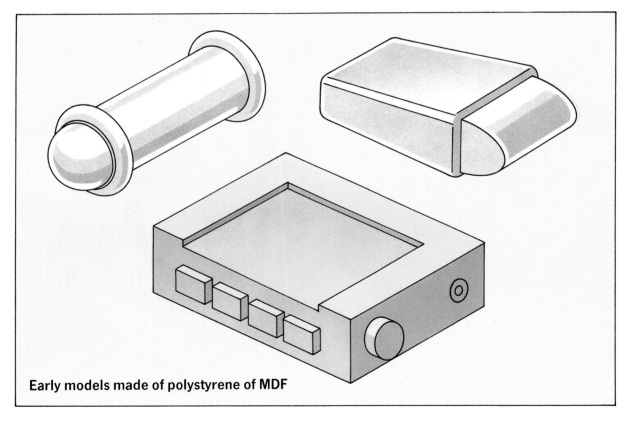

Early models made of polystyrene of MDF

Prototypes

A working model produced at the end of the design process is called a prototype. In the school situation this may be as far as the designer is able to take the project. If earlier models have been made and tested, the prototype should meet the requirements of the client.

In industry, this working prototype may be the first of many models that will be discussed, tested, altered, and retested, before finally going into production.

Working prototypes need to be made to represent the 'real' product as nearly as possible. The materials, the production methods, and the finish all need to be modelled accurately. If they are not, the prototype may not act in the same way as the final product will, so tests on the prototype may miss flaws that the consumer will find.

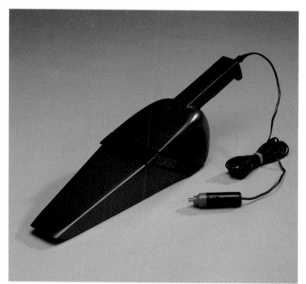

A professionally made model

● Using plasticine or a similar material, make a model of a handle of a garden trowel that will be comfortable for young people of your age to use.

● Using polystyrene, make a model of a telephone handset. This model should be full size, so that you can check that it will be comfortable for most people to use.

Testing product performance

When a product is designed and manufactured, either in school or in industry, it will need to work and should be a pleasure for the user to operate. It will need to be effective, efficient, and safe.

The designer needs to answer these questions:

■ are the materials used in the product strong enough?

■ is there too much material in the product, making it more expensive than need be?

■ will parts of the product wear out too soon?

■ how long will the product last?

■ what are the running costs of the product?

■ does the product carry out the job it is meant to?

■ is the product safe?

To find answers, various tests are carried out. The earlier in the design process that tests are done, the less complicated it is to make modifications. Some of the important tests can be done during the design stage on small samples.

These include tests on:

■ materials – will they be strong enough? Are they flexible enough? Are they stiff enough? What is the minimum size that each component can be?
■ jointing methods – will they cope with the stresses that will be applied?

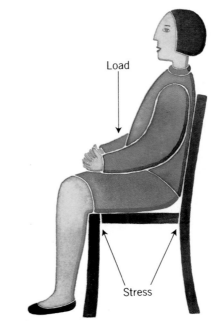

■ finishes – will they stand up to the environment in which they are to be used?

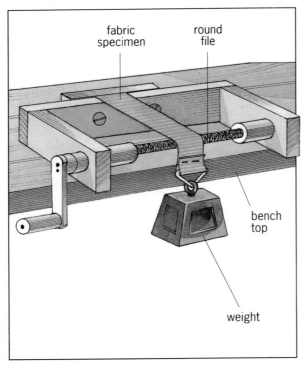

Testing fabric samples

Once the product is in prototype form, other tests can be carried out:

■ is the product comfortable to use?

■ can the product be used safely?

■ is the product efficient?

Testing a food processor

Modifications may need to be made. These may only be minor if:

■ the specification has been written carefully;

■ ergonomic data has been used;

■ safety rules in British Standards have been checked;

■ earlier sample testing has been thorough.

The later in the process that changes need to be made, the more expensive they become.

This prototype testing is most important. At all costs the designer must avoid putting a product into the marketplace that is unsafe or inefficient. The reputation of the designer, and in industry the reputation of the firm he or she works for, rests on the success of the product.

Even once mass production has begun, testing plays an important role. As the components are produced they will be inspected to check that the quality of the product is kept within the specified limit.

A quality inspector at work

Evaluation

Evaluation is a continuous process. As you have read earlier, a designer will have evaluated the research, the two-dimensional ideas, and the various models throughout developing an answer to the brief. The designer may have been able to have helpful comments from the client at various stages.

Once the product has been produced, the designer will need to evaluate how well the prototype meets the specification and satisfies the client. Designers both in school and in industry will:

■ test the end prototype themselves;

■ give it to the client to test;

■ give it to the consumer to test.

Evaluation is concerned with looking at the results of various tests, and coming to some conclusions to see where the product is successful and in which areas there is room for improvement. If you have designed a product for young children, then they need to test your product. If you have designed your product for a disabled person, then that person needs to use it.

Results from the tests can be collected by analysing test results, using questionnaires, and interviewing users.

In industry the results of the evaluation will be written up as part of an evaluation report for the client. In school the results will be part of an evaluation report for the teacher.

Important points

Your prototype evaluation should include:

■ your reasons for choosing your final idea;

■ how well your final design matches your specification;

■ what modification you would make to improve your prototype, if you were to make another one.

Recording methods

You will need to record your findings in one or more of the following ways:

■ detailed but concise written notes;

■ photographs of your product in use. This can be a useful way of showing areas of your product that could be improved;

■ video of your product in use;

■ tape recorded interviews with people who have tested your product;

■ sketches plus notes to explain proposed improvements.

ASSIGNMENTS

● Take a design sheet that is full of different ideas that you have recently completed for a project.

    a) In red pen, make comments about all the things that are good about your designs.

    b) In a different colour, make comments about the bad points in your designs.

● Imagine you are designing a wheelbarrow. Make a list of the points that you would consider essential to cover in order to create a successful design.

Working out the cost

One major piece of information which the designer must consider when making decisions about different ways of answering a design brief is what it will cost to produce the product. Working this cost out will require the designer to consider a number of different aspects of the product:

■ the cost of all the materials involved;

■ the cost of making the tools which will be needed to make the product;

■ the cost of the wages for the people making the product;

■ the cost of the maintenance of the production equipment;

■ the cost of packaging, delivering, and presenting the product.

Elements that make up the cost of a product

The cost of the materials and tools should be worked out for each article produced, and this **unit cost** or cost per article will change depending on the quantity of goods to be produced. For a production run of 200 articles, the total cost of the tools to make the product will be the same as for a production run of 2000 articles, so the unit cost will be higher.

In many cases, mathematics can help the designer to work out whether a product will be profitable for the company to make. For example, a graph could be drawn to show the cost of making the product against the production quantity. This would indicate what the selling price should be in order to make a profit when differing quantities are produced.

Vacuum forming – tools like this are part of a product's cost

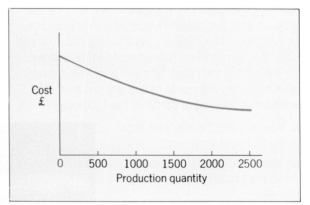

Working out the selling price for different production quantities

For a product to be successful, it is necessary for the designer to make sure that the cost of the product is just right, so that the product will make a profit for the company.

ASSIGNMENTS

● Imagine you are designing a plastic drinks container, to be made on an injection moulding machine. The cost of plastic in granule form is £50 per 1000 kg. To make each container, 0.5 kg of plastic is required. Additional costs for tools, labour, packaging, etc. work out at £1000 per 2000 units produced.

If you wish to design the product to make a profit of 50 per cent on each container, how much would they need to be sold for?

● Explain why the cost of producing an article comes down as the volume produced increases. List as many factors as you can, and indicate which ones are the most significant in reducing the cost of a product.

● Draw up a list of all the parts required to make a ballpoint pen. Given that each ballpoint costs about 10 pence to buy, how much do you think each component costs? What do you think the profit made on each pen is likely to be?

Marketing

If a product is going to be successful, the designer will need to know who is likely to purchase the article which is being designed. This information will have been collected and studied as part of the initial research before the design work starts.

Marketing a product is concerned with deciding how to offer a product for sale to the customer. In most companies there will be a number of people who are specialists in this type of work. They will discuss with the designer how new products are developing while they are being designed, to make sure that the product fulfils a need in the market for which it is intended. This will also help them to plan how they are going to sell the product. This will involve looking at some of the following:

- who are the people who are going to buy the product?

- where can these people be contacted through advertising material?

- how many people are there who might buy the product?

- how can the people be encouraged to buy the product?

- what features of the product make it desirable and better than other similar products from different companies?

- how can the messages about the product be communicated – through TV adverts, newspaper adverts, leaflets to selected housing areas?

Many of these questions will have been answered while the product is being designed, mainly by looking at the market research.

Marketing must be planned if it is to stay within the overall budget for the development of the product. Selling a product can be very expensive, and will reduce the immediate profit which can be made on a product by the company – though its aim is to increase the total profit by increasing sales.

The shops that will sell the product will need to be decided. Depending on the types of shop which are used, display stands and advertising will be designed and produced. The packaging for a product will also be developed to suit the market. It would not be very successful if an expensive watch, designed for the top end of the market, were sold in a cheap cardboard box!

Customer support should also be considered. An after-sales service is important for products which may need servicing after a period of time. Repairing products which are under guarantee is often necessary.

Correct marketing is very important to the success of a product. The designer of a product needs to understand marketing, and to make sure that the marketing specialists understand the features of a product under development, so that they will be communicated to the people who buy the product.

A S S I G N M E N T S

- Draw up what you think would be a good plan for marketing the following products:
  a) an expensive gold and diamond bracelet.
  b) a small, cheap, but sporty motor car aimed at young people.
  c) a new hairdryer for girls and women with long hair.
Use the following headings for your answer on each of the products:
  Advertising materials;
  Point of sale display;
  Packaging for the product;
  Where it would be sold.

- Take two products which satisfy the same need. Describe for each product the market for which it was intended. How was the product advertised?

Presentation drawings

Presentation drawings are only done when the designer has a fairly firm idea of what the product may look like. This is because this type of drawing can take a long time to produce. Presentation drawings can be a very useful way of 'selling' the idea of your solution to your client or teacher. The drawing needs to represent the product as accurately as possible. It is important that information is clearly and attractively presented, and can be easily understood. Some clients will not understand working drawings on their own.

There are a number of ways the right result can be achieved:

■ a perspective line drawing of the product;

■ a large photograph of the product;

■ a colour photocopy of a photograph of the product;

■ a drawing or photograph showing the product in its intended environment;

■ a coloured perspective drawing of the product on its own;

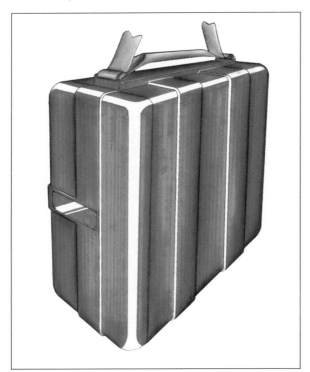

■ a combination of orthographic and perspective views;

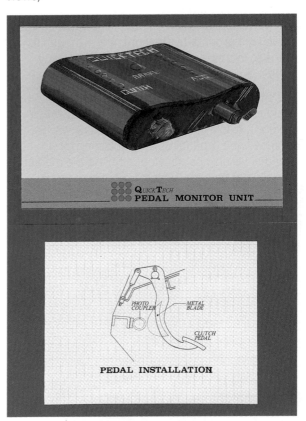

■ a drawing or photograph showing the product in use.

Engineering drawings are used by the designer to communicate details of products to engineers. The engineers will be responsible for producing the tools which make the product's components, and for the manufacture, assembly, and packaging of the product before it is delivered to the consumer.

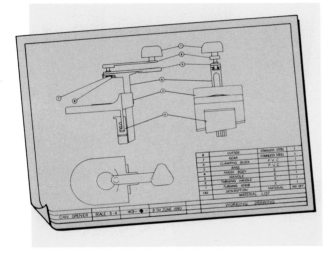

Engineering drawings are normally produced only after some initial design work has been completed. Ideas might need to be communicated to a model maker who will require such information as the size of the part, what finish is to be used, and how the parts fit together.

There are very clear rules for producing engineering drawings. These are described by a British Standards publication, currently referred to as BS 308. This shows the designer how to draw in a way which will be understood by other designers and engineers.

Engineering drawings can be produced using computer systems. This has a number of advantages, as the drawings can be:

■ modified easily and then plotted (drawn out with an electro-mechanical plotter) quickly, to produce a drawing with new information added;

■ looked at by several designers at the same time on different computers;

■ used to provide information to drive machine tools to make a component.

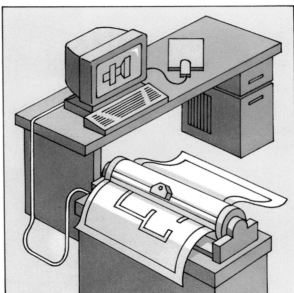

A computer workstation and plotter

Designers normally have to be able to understand engineering drawings in order to communicate with other designers or engineers. The British Standard which these drawings are linked to is very similar to engineering drawing standards in other countries, so this form of drawing can be used to communicate information about products to different countries.

Engineering drawings

55

Project reports

Designers in both schools and industry need to produce a project report. Although this document should be as detailed as possible, it should also be concise. It needs to be logically organized, not a long, rambling essay.

In fact, a report may not even be in written form. It may be a talk, or even a video or tape recording with slides.

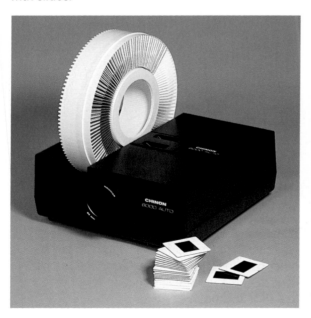

In getting together the information for the report, the designer needs to think about the person or people who will receive the report. What is their background? How much technical information will they understand?

To be successful, you will need to break down the report into several sections. There are several ways of doing this and, as with the design process that you are describing, no one way is correct.

A useful strategy is to use key words as headings for the report. This is one suggestion for the structure:

begin with the background	*need/idea*
talk about the	*design brief/specification*
define and list	*considerations/constraints*
explain the development of	*research/ideas/solutions*
talk about	*process – design/problems*
talk about	*process – production/ problems/modifications*
evaluate	*successes/effectiveness/ weaknesses*
suggest	*answers* to any problems found in final prototype
indicate	*costing* – as thoroughly as possible

Some of the key sections in a report

A report will take a while to organize, so do not leave it till the last minute. A report is your chance of showing how thoroughly you have tackled the project. Before you attempt to produce the final copy of your report, read the section on displays (pages 58–9), as your report will form an important part of your display.

Displays

Anyone who displays their work, whether it is goods, products, or paintings, is doing it for one main reason – to communicate an image. It may be your own work for an examiner, or it may be to try to get others to buy a product.

Displaying your work, whether it is for your teacher, your examiner, or your client, is a most important task for the designer of products. As with all your design work you need to take pride in what you do.

You must think about the person who is going to look at your display. The display needs to be tailored to that person. If your display is at school, your teacher will need to see everything that you did throughout the project, including all your initial rough sketches. If you are a designer in industry, your client will only be interested in the end product, the final drawings, and a report.

A display of design work

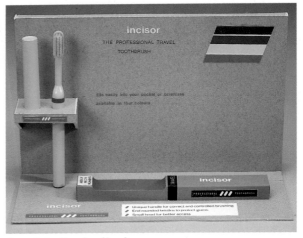

A point of sale display

It is most important that your display is welcoming, looks crisp, and tells a clear story. It needs to give your product the edge. Your product may be virtually the same as other people's, but your display could sell it.

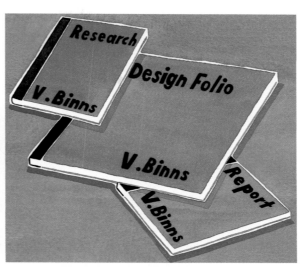

Presentation displays of different perfumes

Your display should be uncluttered. To achieve this, you may decide that it is a good idea to present some of your 2D work in a series of folders:

- research, and evaluation of that research;
- initial rough sketches;
- report.

You will then have presentation drawings and possibly working drawings to display on a display board, and all your models and the final product to display on a flat surface.

The display must not look like a random collection of work. There are various methods of achieving continuity. The use of colour can help (but used unwisely it can also hinder the image you may require). Mount all your displayed work on the same coloured background. Bind all your folders in the same way, and use the same typeface on all your lettering.

Remember, displaying work is not a last-minute thing. It takes longer to put a display together than you think.

ASSIGNMENTS

- Design a front cover that will be suitable for your latest design project. It could be used for one or more of the following:
  a) your research.
  b) your design work.
  c) your report.

- Take an imaginary chocolate bar. Give it a name. Produce a design for a shop display to appeal to the teenage market. Remember shop space is at a premium and your display will need to be compact.

Case study 1

Designers	Fourth-year pupils
School	Rawlins Community College
Client	Ladkin Hosiery
Background	The school is situated in a textile region. The Leicester and District Knitwear Industries Association and Ladkin Hosiery, together with the school, worked out a design brief.
Brief	To design an original motif for socks for Ladkin Hosiery for their spring/summer collection.
Specification	This included information on themes to be used (the client specified vegetables as a theme), as well as on colours, age, and gender range. It also gave essential technical data, such as number of stitches and rows, length and circumference, size of design, and maximum number of colours per row.
Research	The designers investigated the following:

- the market for this product;
- division of labour;
- mass production;
- automation;
- marketing;
- safety;
- the responsibility of designing for the mass market.

Mr Ladkin of Ladkin Hosiery came to the school on a number of occasions to advise the young designers and monitor their progress.

Designing

The following key stages were completed:

1 Initial sketches of vegetables were made, using libraries and greengrocers.
2 Interpretational drawings were made, modifying and simplifying the sketches.
3 Designs were transferred to blank sock outlines to achieve the correct scale.
4 From these drawings, numbers of rows and stiches were worked out.
5 A stitch-by-stitch coloured graph outline was produced.

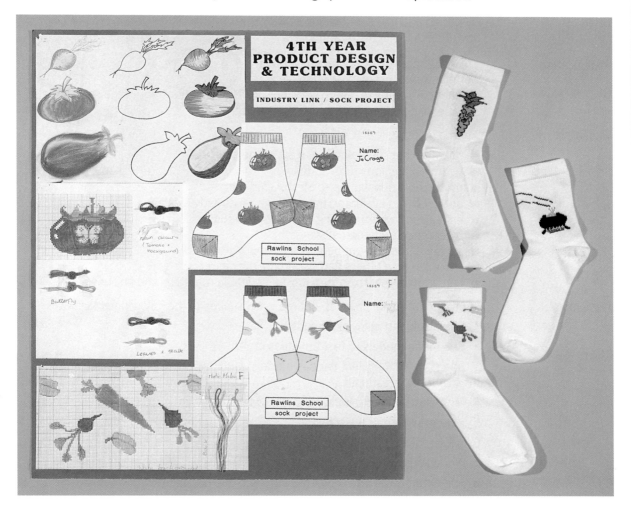

Evaluation

Pupils set up displays of their work. These were evaluated by teachers and a team from Ladkin Hosiery, who chose a number of designs for making up as samples.

Making

The pupils went to the factory to input their designs into a computer and produce a data cassette. They programmed the knitting machines and, under careful supervision, produced a batch run of their sock design.

After the project was completed, pupils were kept informed about the success of their design work.

Case study 2

Designer	Andrea Cooper, a fifth-year pupil
School	Burleigh College
Client	The principal of Burleigh College
Background	This design project was tackled by Andrea Cooper as her major project for her GCSE examination.
Brief	To design and make an outside seating unit for Burleigh College students.
Specification	The seating unit was to be comfortable, durable, vandalproof, cost-effective and aesthetically suitable. There were not only specifications about the seat, but also situational considerations to be taken into account.

Research

Andrea investigated as follows:

- talked to the client and the users of the seat;
- gathered opinions from staff;
- produced a questionnaire for the students;
- analysed and evaluated the seating that already existed;
- established where seating was most needed;
- researched architectual trends;
- surveyed the environment of the school grounds;
- looked at how others had solved the problem;
- researched **anthropometrics**, and suitable materials and finishes.

Designing

In producing a final product, Andrea was involved in the following activities:

1 She produced many sketch ideas.

2 She made models to test out ideas in 3D.

3 She showed the client various models, and made modifications as a result of the client's suggestions.

4 More models and details were worked out.

5 Various materials were tested.

6 She received the client's approval of the final design model.

7 Working drawings and costing were approved.

8 She organized a brick layer to help her make her solution.

Prototype

The unit was made in three days:
day 1 – foundations dug and timber (Iroko) collected.
day 2 – brick construction built.
day 3 – bin made, brickwork finished, and plants added.

Evaluation

The design answered the brief. It looked good, it met the budget cost, it fitted into the environment, and the students found it comfortable. Only time will tell whether it is vandalproof and durable.

Case study 3

Designer	Paul Saville, final-year student
University	Department of Design and Technology, Loughborough University of Technology
Client	Faces Designs on Mountains
Background	This design project was Paul's major piece of work during his final year on the BA (Hons) Degree in Design and Technology. His personal interest in climbing encouraged him to look for a client with a design brief he could tackle.

Brief	To design and develop a self-belaying (device for controlling a safety rope) which would enable a climber to climb solo, but at the same time use a rope and runners in the normal manner. The device was to take the place of the lead climber's partner as far as belaying is concerned, so that in the event of a fall the climber's rapid descent would be stopped.
Specification	The product was to be safe and easy to use, have minimum drag, stop the falling climber, have no sharp edges, and work on dry, wet, or iced rope.
Initial research	Paul investigated the following areas: ■ existing methods of climbing, and the part played by a belayer in the process; ■ properties and construction of climbing ropes; ■ existing mechanisms to control rope slippage; ■ size and direction of loading (force) caused by a falling climber; ■ attitude of climbers to a self-belaying device.
Designing	Paul did a **feasibility study** and tested existing equipment. Then he developed a number of simple mechanisms and constructed them as wooden models. He made up an inertia system in 2D and 3D models. He used mathematical modelling to ensure that all parts would withstand the forces applied to them.
Prototype	Paul developed a working prototype to evaluate the final design. He used aircraft aluminium (which has a high strength to density value) and mild steel for internal components. He suggested to the client a number of manufacturing methods for the final product.
Evaluation	The device was then tested using light loads, adjusting the strength of the spring till it could be loaded fully. The next stage was for Paul to test the device in use while climbing.

The client approved of the design, and took out a patent on the device. The client is now developing the device further, and it should go into production in the near future.

Glossary

Aesthetics	Aspects of a product concerned with beauty or style.
Anthropometrics	The measurement of factors concerned with the human body.
Budget	A plan for spending where a fixed sum of money is available for a project.
British Standards Institute (BSI)	An official organization in the UK which creates written sets of standards that designers and manufacturers must conform to when designing and testing products.
Brief	A clear description of the task which the designer has to tackle.
Client	A person or company that has a need for a solution to a design brief.
Computer integrated manufacturing system (CIM)	A computer-based system for the total design and manufacture of a product.
Consultant	A person or team of people with expertise who will advise or help others.
Corporate identity	A designed image that represents a company and its business to the public.
Design sheet	A sheet of drawings, notes, and diagrams produced by a designer during the design process.
Elevation	An orthographic view (see **orthographic projection**) of the front or end of an object.
Evaluate	To assess information, ideas, and proposals for solutions throughout the design process.
Ergonomics	The analysis and evaluation of products, environments, and procedures that involve people.
Feasibility study	Gathering together information to check whether a design brief can be solved.
Human factors	See **ergonomics**.
Logo	A designed, two-dimensional image forming part of a corporate identity.
Marketing	Attracting buyers for products which are offered for sale.
Mathematical modelling	Using mathematics to prove that an idea will work.
Mind map	A series of written linked thoughts, usually starting from one central concept.
Orthographic projection	A series of flat views of an object showing it exactly as it is in shape and size.
Prototype	A model that is visually identical to the finished product and which also works like the finished product.
Scale	Drawing and making models either larger or smaller than life size.
Simulation	A working model of a process or situation that would be too complex or expensive to build and test while designing.
Specification	A list of the important factors which must be considered for a product.
Strength to density value	A comparison between the mechanical strength and the density of a material.
Styling	The exterior form of a product; designing and producing this form.
System	An integrated series of component parts.
Tensile test	A test that shows how a material behaves when stretched.
Unit cost	The cost of one item.